The *Cheers* Trivia Book

The *Cheers* Trivia Book

Mark Wenger

A Citadel Press Book

Published by Carol Publishing Group

To all of the "characters" in our
everyday lives who make us laugh.

A Citadel Press Book
Published by Carol Publishing Group
Citadel Press is a registered trademark of Carol Communications, Inc.
Editorial Offices: 600 Madison Avenue, New York, N.Y. 10022
Sales and Distribution Offices: 120 Enterprise Avenue, Secaucus,
    N.J. 07094
In Canada: Canadian Manda Group, P.O. Box 920, Station U, Toronto,
    Ontario M8Z 5P9
Queries regarding rights and permissions should be addressed to Carol
Publishing Group, 600 Madison Avenue, New York, N.Y. 10022

Carol Publishing Group books are available at special discounts for
bulk purchases, sales promotions, fund-raising, or educational
purposes. Special editions can be created to specifications.
For details, contact Special Sales Department, Carol Publishing Group,
120 Enterprise Avenue,
Secaucus, N.J. 07094

Manufactured in the United States of America
10   9   8   7   6   5   4   3   2   1

Library of Congress Cataloging-in-Publication Data

Wenger, Mark.
    The Cheers trivia book / Mark Wenger.
        p.   cm.
    "A Citadel Press book."   ISBN 0–8065–1482–5
    1. Cheers (Television program)—Miscellanea.   I. Title.
PN1992.77.C473W45   1994
791.45'72—dc20   93–45402
                                                          CIP

Contents

My heartfelt appreciation to my wife for her support and patience. My sincere gratitude to Bob Wilczynski for his encouragement and suggestions. And my indebtedness to Allan J. Wilson and Carol Publishing for taking a chance on a first-time writer.

Introduction

Cheers was one of the longest-running and most popular television shows ever. Though this book is filled with questions that will challenge your memory, its primary intention is to help you relive the most hilarious moments of this highly acclaimed comedy.

Laugh at Norm's one-liners, Cliff's little-known facts, Woody's barnyard wisdom, and the outrageous practical jokes. Remember Sam's irrepressible come-on lines, Carla's stinging insults, and Frasier's bar-side psychoanalysis.

Recall Sam and Diane's on-again, off-again romance and Rebecca's endless pursuit of a millionaire, and once again enjoy the laughs and tears of the all-too-short final season and the grand-finale show.

For those of you who do aspire to test your *Cheers* knowledge, the scale on the following page will help rate your skill.

Cheers Trivia Rating Scale

Correct Answers	Award
600 or more	**The Cliff Clavin Award:** You know it all (or at least claim you do), and are only too happy to prove it.
500–599	**The Carla Tortelli Award:** You achieved this level not on your knowledge, but because you cheated.
400–499	**The Frasier Crane Award:** Though not completely interested, your desire for barfly companionship helped you reach this level.
300–399	**The Sam & Diane Award:** You could have scored much higher if you had not been arguing so much.

200–299   **The Norm Peterson Award:** You have spent way too much time at *Cheers*, and only got the beer questions correct.

100–199   **The Woody & Coach Award:** You're lovable, but you need to pay more attention to life around you.

0   **The Lilith Sternin Crane Award:** You could have won it all, but you refused to play along.

The *Cheers* Trivia Book

1

Where Everybody Knows Your Name

Questions

1. In what city is the Cheers bar supposed to be located?

2. According to the Cheers sign above the bar's entrance, in what year was the bar established?

3. What was the original name of the bar, before it became Cheers?

4. What is the name of the restaurant above Cheers?

5. What was Sam's occupation before owning the bar?

6. For what team did Sam play?

7. What was Sam's nickname?

8. As a relief pitcher, Sam was called in to save the game with his "Slider of Death." Who gave the pitch its name?
   A. The opposing hitters
   B. Sam's teammates
   C. The game announcer

9. What ruined Sam's baseball career?

10. What kind of car did Sam have and what color was it?

11. What part of Sam's body was insured?

12. What grooming aids did Sam keep behind the bar?

13. What alphabetical resource was extremely valuable to Sam?

14. With which of the following types of women did Sam say he would never get involved?
    A. Married
    B. Underage
    C. Comatose
    D. All of the above

15. What is the name of the real bar in Boston on which *Cheers* was based?

16. In what year did *Cheers* debut?

17. In the *Cheers* debut, what was its ranking among the seventy-seven TV shows that appeared that week?
    A. 1st
    B. 10th
    C. 77th

18. Who created and produced *Cheers*?

19. Who directed most of the shows?

20. Whose real-life sister, Heide, wrote many of the shows?

21. Old-fashioned pictures were shown in the opening credits of the show. One man was holding a newspaper. What was its bold headline?

Shelley Long, left, as a teaching assistant who becomes a cocktail waitress to expand her horizons, and Ted Danson, right, as the owner of the sports-oriented bar where she works, in the premiere season of *Cheers*. (*AP/Wide World Photos*)

22. Who wrote the lyrics and music to the *Cheers* theme song?

23. Who sang the theme song?

24. What are the words to the chorus of the theme song used to open each show?

25. What political talk show host moderated the 200th anniversary special?

26. What former cast member returned for the 200th anniversary special?

27. What sportscaster and late-night talk show host the *Cheers* retrospective prior to the last show?

28. What late-night talk show host hosted the *Cheers* cast following the last show?

29. *Cheers* has received 119 Emmy nominations. How does this rank among all other TV shows?

30. *Cheers* has received 28 Emmy awards. How does this rank among all other TV shows?

Answers

1. Boston

2. 1895

3. Mom's

4. Melville's

5. Professional baseball player

6. The Boston Red Sox

7. May Day Malone

8. B. Sam's teammates

9. He was an alcoholic.

10. '64 Corvette, flame red

11. His hair

12. His cologne and comb

13. His little black book

14. D. All of the above

15. The Bull & Finch

16. 1982

17. C. 77th

18. Glen and Les Charles and James Burrows

19. James Burrows

20. Rhea Perlman

21. WE WIN!

22. Judy Hart Angelo and Gary Portnoy

23. Gary Portnoy

24. "Sometimes you want to go where everybody knows your name, and they're always glad you came. You want to be where you can see the troubles are all the same. You want to go where everybody knows your name."

25. John McLaughlin

26. Shelley Long

27. Bob Costas

28. Jay Leno

29. First

30. Second

2

The Early Years

Questions

1. While drunk, Sam made a bet to marry a particular woman or give up his bar. Whom was he supposed to marry?

2. Who bet in the football pool based on uniform color, state flowers, and cities with symphonies conducted by foreign-born conductors?

3. What did Diane claim that Sam wrote on the bottom of his shoes?

4. Who taught Diane to close the bar at night?

5. A man with six months to live enjoyed his time at Cheers so much that he decided to give the gang $100,000. On what did he write his amended will?
   A. A piece of paper
   B. A cocktail napkin
   C. Norm's shirt

6. Sam donated his baseball jersey to a public-television auction. When it did not sell, who bought it the first time?

7. Who bought his jersey the second time?

8. To persuade Carla to go to the Gala Postman's Ball with him, Cliff offered her a VCR. When Cliff changed his mind about the date, what did he offer her to go with someone else instead?

9. On the way home from the ball with Diane, what did Cliff pretend to do?

10. Once Diane claimed that she never received the same exuberant greeting as Norm. The next time she entered the bar, what did everyone shout?

11. After the gang had excluded Diane from a number of events, they decided to make it up to her. Where did they take her?
   A. The opera
   B. An elegant restaurant
   C. A French film festival

12. When Norm and Cliff went to a baseball game, they sat in the center-field seats and took off their shirts. Why were they asked to change seats?

13. When a slumping pitcher asked Sam for help, Sam gave him his lucky charm. What was it?

14. Where did Sam get his lucky charm?

15. What did the charm help him to do?

16. When Frasier was searching for an anniversary gift for Lilith, Norm suggested that he get her a "mank." What was it?

The long-awaited marriage of Sam Malone (Ted Danson) and Diane Chambers (Shelley Long) appears at hand in the 1987 season finale and the farewell appearance of Shelley Long. (*AP/Wide World Photos*)

17. Coach's niece, Joyce, came to Boston to go to college. Her father sent a request with her to Sam. What did he ask Sam to do?
    A. Stay away from her
    B. Find her a nice boy to date
    C. Take care of her

18. Sam thought Woody would be a good match for Joyce. What did Woody and Joyce decide to do, which upset Sam?

19. When Cliff was feeling sick, Norm offered to deliver the rest of his mail for him. What happened?

20. When Sam was on a radio call-in show, what did Woody call to ask him?
    A. The combination to the safe
    B. If he could leave early
    C. Where Sam put the olives

21. A customer claimed to be a spy, and then a poet, and then a millionaire who offered to buy the bar. Which was he?

22. How much did Diane claim that Sam spent on a large bottle of his cologne?
    A. $2.50
    B. $15.00
    C. $50.00

23. When Sam's brother Derrick visited, what feelings for him did Sam reveal?

24. What was his brother's occupation?

25. How did Derrick travel?

26. Which of the following did Derrick do while at the bar?
    A. He tap-danced.
    B. He performed trick pool shots.
    C. He taught Spanish to Coach.
    D. All of the above

27. When Diane threatened to go to Europe with Derrick, how did she "torture" Sam into revealing his feelings for her?
    A. She pulled his hair.
    B. She refused to stop talking.
    C. She scratched her nails on a chalkboard.

28. After listening to Diane boast about her poetry, Sam managed to get a poem published. However, he did admit to copying it from someone. Who?

29. What did Norm and Cliff do with new issues of *People* magazine?

30. Diane made Sam realize that he was too competitive after he played in a charity baseball game and struck out the entire opposing team. Who made up the opposing team?

31. Sam made Diane realize that she was too competitive by challenging her to a game that neither one would then concede. What game?

32. When Cliff sold shoes to the guys, he claimed the shoes were precisely machine-measured. What did he have them do to determine their correct foot size?
    A. They measured their feet with a ruler.
    B. They each sent a shoe from each person to the factory.
    C. They traced their feet on a cocktail napkin.

33. When the guys tried on their new shoes, what defect did they find?

34. For what type of diploma did Sam return to school?

35. Why did Sam get the highest grades in the class?

36. What memory tip did Coach share with Sam to help him study?

37. Norm suggested a new business venture to his friends. It was a combination Laundromat and what?

38. Sam started feeling old when he had what type of an operation?

39. What western movie did the gang always watch at Sam's place?

40. What did Diane wear to Thanksgiving dinner at Carla's?

41. When the turkey took too long to cook, tempers began to flare and a fight started. What kind of fight?

42. When Vera finally arrived at the Thanksgiving dinner, what prevented everyone from seeing her face?

Answers

1. Jacqueline Bisset

2. Diane

3. "R" for right and "L" for left

4. Norm

5. B. A cocktail napkin

6. Diane

7. Sam

8. A big-screen TV

9. Run out of gas

10. Norm!

11. A. The opera

12. The glare from Norm's skin was blinding the batters.

13. A bottle cap

14. It was from the last bottle of beer that Sam drank.

15. It kept him from drinking again.

16. A mock mink

17. C. Take care of her

18. They decided to live together.

19. Norm was arrested for mail fraud.

20. C. Where Sam put the olives

21. A millionaire

22. A. $2.50

23. He felt inferior to Derrick.

24. An international lawyer

25. In his own jet

26. D. All of the above

27. C. She scratched her nails on a chalkboard.

28. Diane

29. They blackened the teeth of celebrities.

30. Playboy playmates

31. Ping-Pong

32. C. He traced their feet on a cocktail napkin.

33. All of the shoes squeaked.

34. High school

35. He was dating the teacher.

36. He sang geography facts to music.

37. Tanning salon

38. Hernia

39. _The Magnificent Seven_

40. A Pilgrim-era outfit

41. A food fight

42. She was hit in the face with a pie.

3

Diane

Questions

1. Who played the part of Diane Chambers?

2. What was Diane's occupation when she first came to Cheers?

3. Which of the following was *not* one of Diane's college majors?
   A. Psychology
   B. Literature
   C. Anthropology
   D. Art History
   E. Poetry
   F. French
   G. Indian Studies
   H. Manchurian Folk Dancing
   I. She majored in all of the above.

4. Diane first appeared with Sumner Sloan, a college professor. What were Diane and Sumner on their way to do?

5. What happened to Sumner?

6. For what reasons did Sam offer Diane a job?
   A. She needed a job.
   B. She had a good memory for drink orders.
   C. She asked for a job.

7. Diane's father stipulated in his will that Diane had to do something within ten years after his death or Diane's mother would lose her share of the estate. What was Diane required to do?

8. Who attempted to help Diane fulfill her father's request?

9. Who eventually came to the financial aid of Diane's mother?

10. What was the name of Diane's cat?
   A. Elizabeth Barrett Browning
   B. Aphrodite
   C. Diane

11. What did Sam do when Diane bragged about her reservations at an exclusive restaurant?

12. How did Sam get into the restaurant?
   A. He impersonated a famous gourmet.
   B. He bribed the maitre d'.
   C. He used his baseball connections.

13. What did Sam do when he could not pay for his meal?

14. After Sam loaned Diane money to buy a rare book, he became interested in the book and began to read it. He then damaged the book. How?

15. Why did Diane agree to be in a barmaids' contest?
   A. To denounce all female contests
   B. To win a trip to Bermuda
   C. To prove she was a good waitress

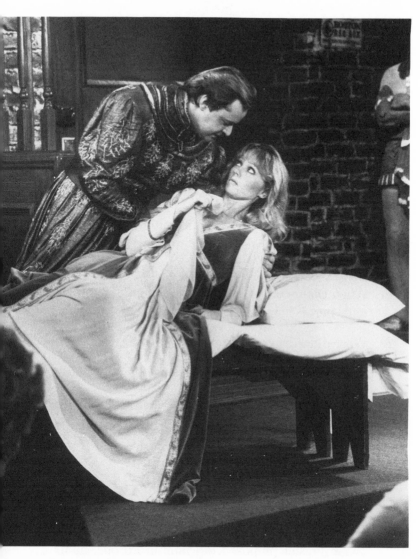

While playing Desdemona in the strangulation scene from
"Othello," Diane thinks she may be in trouble with her costar,
Andy (Derek McGrath), the ex-convict she coached for an
acting debut at Cheers. (*AP/Wide World Photos*)

16. What did Diane do when she won the contest and the trip?

17. To smooth over an argument with Diane, Sam decided to have a portrait painted for Diane. Whom was the portrait of?

18. What happened after Diane had the portrait done?

19. After Sam and Diane broke up, Diane went to a sanatorium. To what old habit did Sam return?

20. Sam unknowingly went out with one of Diane's friends from her mental institution. From what did the friend suffer?

21. When Diane returned to the bar, whom did she bring with her to help Sam?

22. What did Frasier's mother ask Diane to do?

23. To what did Diane believe she was allergic when she moved in with Frasier?

24. What other symptom did Diane have, other than sneezing?

25. To what did Sam think Diane was allergic?

26. As Diane was leaving for Europe, what did Sam offer her as an alternative to Frasier's security?

27. When Frasier proposed to Diane in Europe, he took her to an Italian restaurant. However, the staff of the restaurant was very upset about something. What?

28. In what country were Frasier and Diane to be married?

29. What did Sam do when he heard Frasier and Diane were going to marry?

30. After Diane left Frasier at the altar, he sought revenge against Sam. Frasier pulled a gun on Sam, but Sam knew it wasn't loaded. Why?

31. After Diane left Fraiser, she gallivanted though Europe. When she returned to the United States, where did she end up?

32. After Sam found Diane, what did he unsuccessfully look for in her place of employment?

33. While gallivanting through Europe, Diane met an adventurer in Spain named Jack Dalton. At what event did they meet?

34. What happened when Sam and Diane went for a ride on Jack's jet?

35. Sam and Diane created a plan to restore Frasier's self-confidence. Sam pretended to be depressed and asked Frasier for counseling. What was Frasier's diagnosis, which turned out to be quite accurate?

36. For what type of dance did Diane audition?

37. What did Frasier do with the dance instructor's negative analysis of Diane?

38. What four-letter word did Sam have trouble saying to Diane?

39. While Sam and Diane were in the midst of breaking up over a fortune from a fortune-telling scale, one more fortune popped out. What did it say?

    A. "Break up."
    B. "Marry each other."
    C. "Machine empty, order more fortunes today."

40. After Sam began dating a city councilwoman, what did she want Sam to do about Diane?

41. During a city council press conference, with Sam onstage and Diane in the audience, what did they do?
    A. They insulted each other.
    B. They made funny faces at each other,
    C. They threw things at each other.

42. When the gang realized that Sam was going to propose to Diane, which two people screamed in horror?

43. Where were Sam and Diane when Sam proposed the first time?

44. Where were Sam and Diane when Sam proposed the second time?

45. What did Sam force Diane to do when she turned down his second proposal?

46. When Diane decided to accept Sam's proposal, she went back to the boat in a sexy nightgown to surprise Sam. Whom did she find on the boat?

47. Where were Sam and Diane when Sam proposed the third time?

48. What happened to Diane after she turned down Sam's third proposal?

49. For what was Sam arrested following the third marriage proposal?

50. Why did Sam propose to Diane in court?

51. Sumner (Diane's former fiancé) returned under the pretense of seeking Diane's forgiveness. What was his real intention?

52. In an effort to converse with Sumner and Diane, Sam decided to read a literary classic. What did he read?
    A. *War and Peace*
    B. *The Catcher in the Rye*
    C. *Alice in Wonderland*

53. Sam and Diane had a session with a famous marriage counselor who was a friend of Frasier's. What was the counselor's advice?

54. Sam and Diane bought a house from an elderly couple. What did they do to help the couple and their grandchildren in their transition from the house?

55. What picture did Sam insist on hanging in their new house?
    A. Dogs playing poker
    B. Himself in his baseball uniform
    C. His Corvette

56. What did Sam dream about that convinced him to marry Diane?

57. Where did Sam plan to take Diane on their honeymoon?

58. What did Sam insist that Diane do instead of marrying him?

59. What were Sam's last words to Diane as she left the bar after they had called off their wedding?

Answers

1. Shelley Long

2. College student

3. I. She majored in all of the above.

4. Get married in Barbados

5. He took his wife to Barbados instead.

6. A. and B. She needed a job *and* she had a good memory for drink orders.

7. Get married

8. Sam

9. Boggs, the chauffeur

10. A. Elizabeth Barrett Browning

11. He canceled the reservations.

12. A. He impersonated a famous gourmet.

13. He ran out.

14. He dropped it in the bathtub.

15. A. To denounce all female contests

16. Happily accepted the trip

17. Diane

18. They split up.

19. He began to drink again.

20. She was obsessive about men.

21. Frasier Crane, a psychiatrist

22. To not see Frasier again

23. Frasier's dog

24. She talked in a funny, high-pitched voice.

25. Making a commitment to Frasier

26. One day at a time with Sam

27. They had just had a funeral for their chef.

28. Italy

29. He went to stop them.

30. Sam did not see any bullets in the chambers of the gun.

31. In a convent

32. A men's room

33. The Running of the Bulls

34. Jack faked his death.

35. That Sam and Diane were still in love with each other

36. Ballet

37. He altered it to be flattering.

38. "Love"

39. C. "Machine empty, order more fortunes today."

40. Fire her

41. B. They made funny faces at each other.

42. Carla and Frasier

43. On the telephone

44. On a boat

45. Jump off the boat

46. Sam's friend, a monsignor

47. In the bar

48. She fell and was injured while being chased by Sam.

49. Assault. Sam was accused of causing Diane to fall.

50. The judge made Sam propose or face assault charges.

51. To get Diane back

52. A. *War and Peace*

53. Not to get married and never to see each other again

54. They gave them a Christmas party.

55. A. Dogs playing poker

56. Happily growing old with her

57. Disney World

58. Finish her novel

59. "Have a good life."

4

Coach

Questions

1. Who played the part of Coach?

2. What was Coach's character's name?

3. Why did Coach think everyone called him "Coach"?

4. What baseball record did Coach hold?

5. Why did Coach give names to the bar glasses?

6. What did Coach say he once owned and then lost a bundle on when he finally unloaded it?
   A. Martha's Vineyard
   B. Boston Common
   C. The Old North Church

7. When Coach was losing money to a con man, whom did Sam get to help win the money back?

8. Coach and Sam always watched movies together in which a particular actor starred. Who was the actor?

9. Why did Coach say it was hard for him to get up to Fenway Park to see a baseball game?

10. Which of the following phrases did Coach learn to speak in Spanish?
    A. "How tall is my dentist?"
    B. "What's the score?"
    C. "Do you speak English?"

11. When Coach did not get a coaching job in Venezuela, it was not because they did not like his Spanish. What did they not like?

12. One of Coach's former baseball friends was nicknamed "The Blindman." Coach thought it was because he was blind, but what was the real reason?

13. Coach once said he felt exhausted. Why?
    A. He had to walk to work.
    B. He had to work a second shift.
    C. He dreamt he had insomnia.

14. What would Coach do when he put a telephone caller on hold?

15. What was Coach's reply when asked: "If a tree fell in the woods and there is no one there to hear it, does it make a sound?"

16. When Coach tried to organize the bar's annual picnic, who finally volunteered to head all of the committees?

17. Coach bought a fortune-telling machine from a man he claimed was a cross between:
    A. Kennedy and Nixon
    B. Einstein and John Wayne
    C. Hitler and Lincoln

Cheers cast members, clockwise, Ted Danson, Shelley Long,
Nicholas Colasanto, and Rhea Perlman. (*AP/Wide World
Photos*)

18. What did Sam and Diane try to do when they felt Coach was spending too much time with them?

19. Coach's engagement was broken off when something happened to his fiancée. What?

20. Which of the following was the occupation of Coach's prospective son-in-law?
    A. He sold suits door-to-door.
    B. He sold used cars.
    C. He sold cement.

21. Nicholas Colasanto kept a picture of what Indian in his dressing room?

Answers

1. Nicholas Colasanto

2. Ernie Pantusso

3. Because he never flew first class

4. Most times hit by a pitch

5. So he could tell them apart

6. C. The Old North Church

7. The hustler Harry the Hat

8. Robert Mitchum

9. He kept getting lost.

10. A. "How tall is my dentist?"

11. His English

12. He sold blinds during the off-season.

13. C. He dreamt he had insomnia.

14. Sing into the phone

15. "If there is no one there, how do we know the tree fell down?"

16. Coach

17. C. Hitler and Lincoln

18. They tried to set him up with a woman.

19. She won the lottery.

20. A. He sold suits door-to-door.

21. Geronimo

5

Norm!

Questions

1. Who played the part of Norm Peterson?

2. Whenever Norm entered the bar, what did everyone (except Diane) shout?

3. What did Diane shout?

4. What was Norm's nickname in high school?
   A. Normy
   B. Fatso
   C. Moonglow

5. In what sport did Norm participate during high school?

6. What was Norm's favorite restaurant?
   A. Beefeater's Bonanza
   B. Hungry Heifer
   C. Decadent Delight

7. What reason did Norm give for quitting the Boy Scouts?

8. According to Norm, why did his high school coach tell his players to "give the ball to Peterson"?

9. In what branch of the service did Norm serve?

10. When Norm was told that his chest X ray was clear, where did he insist upon going?
    A. Bora Bora
    B. Hawaii
    C. Home

11. Where did Norm hide instead?

Match the following questions with the correct reply from Norm:

12. "How are you doing today, Mr. Peterson?"

    A. My ideal weight, if I was 11 feet tall."

13. "What are you up to, Norm?"

    B. Never better, but just once I would like to be better."

14. "Hey, what's happening, Norm?"

    C. Let's talk about what's going in Mr. Peterson."

15. "Hey, Mr. P., Jack Frost nipping at your nose?"

    D. "Yes; now let's get Joe Beer nipping at my liver."

16. "What's going on, Mr. Peterson?"

    E. "It's a dog-eat-dog world, and I'm wearing milk-bone underwear."

17. For his birthday, what did the guys give Norm (complete with ribbon)?

18. What did Norm do after he was turned down for a big promotion because the other company wives did not like Vera?

19. What was Norm's reply when asked how far along he was on painting his house?
    A. He was half done.
    B. He bought the paint.
    C. He bought the little painter's hat.

Match the following questions with the correct reply from Norm:

20. "What's going down, Mr. Peterson?"

    A. "Boy meets beer, boy drinks beer, boy gets another beer."

21. "What's the story, Mr. Peterson?"

    B. "Just my usual: I'll have a trough of beer and a snorkel."

22. "What's new, Norm?"

    C. "My cheeks on this bar stool."

23. "How does a beer sound, Norm?"

    D. "Most of my wife."

24. "What will it be, Mr. P.?"

    E. "I don't know—I usually finish them before they get a word in."

25. Why did Norm agree to take a litter of kittens from Carla?

26. To prevent the executives at Norm's company from feeling stressed, what job was given to Norm?

27. Surprisingly, Norm enjoyed Cliff's lodge meeting, until they announced something would be banned from all of their parties. What?

Match the following questions with the correct reply from Norm:

28. (Bartender; with it raining outside) "Still pouring, Norm?"

    A. "The warranty on my liver."

After learning that Diane and Frasier are to be married in Europe, Norm (George Wendt, left), Cliff (John Ratzenberger) and Carla (Rhea Perlman) propose a toast to the happy couple. (*AP/Wide World Photos*)

29. "What can I do for you, Mr. P.?"

    B. "So float a cornflake in it."

30. "How's life in the fast lane, Normy?"

    C. "Funny, I was about to ask you the same thing."

31. "It's a little early for a beer, isn't it?"

    D. "Elope with my wife."

32. "What's up, Norm?"

    E. "Beats me—I can't find the on-ramp."

33. When did Norm say was the last time he cried?
    A. When the bar ran out of beer
    B. When he got a job as a beer taster
    C. When he found out that Vera tricked him into marriage by telling him she was pregnant

34. What animal did Norm use to prove to Cliff that it took little skill to deliver the mail?

Match the following questions with the correct reply from Norm:

35. "What's the story, Norm?"

    A. "You meant nice cold beer going *down* Mr. Peterson."

36. "What do you know there, Norm?"

    B. "Thirsty guy walks into a bar; you finish it."

37. "Beer, Normy?"

    C. "A transfusion with a head on it."

38. "What'll it be, Norm?"   D. "How to sit. How to drink. Want to quiz me?"

39. "Nice cold beer coming up, Mr. Peterson?"   E. "You really know how to make it sound tempting, you fast talker."

40. Which of the following did Norm dislike about visiting Vera's mother?
    A. No beer
    B. No TV
    C. Heat turned up to 80 degrees
    D. All of the above

41. Norm had difficulty playing chess on the office computer because something was taking up most of the computer's memory. What?

42. A client asked Norm if he came to Cheers very often (meaning two or three times a week). What was Norm's reply?

43. When Norm thought he was about to start an affair, he asked Sam if there had been any innovations in a particular industry since 1965. What industry?

44. Which of the following synthetic foods was on the menu at the Hungry Heifer?
    A. Bif
    B. Loobster
    C. Chucken

45. What did Rebecca have Norm do to work off his bar tab?

46. Norm hired some additional painters to help him out, but he had trouble telling them what to do. How did he solve the problem?

47. Why did Norm promise Vera that he would pick up some Chinese food for her?
    A. It was their anniversary.
    B. She hated Chinese food.
    C. He had spilled it on the floor that morning.

Match the following questions with the correct reply from Norm:

48. "How's life treating you, Norm?"

49. "What do you say, Normy?"

50. "Hey, Mr. P., got room for another beer?"

51. "What can I do for you, Norm?"

52. "What's new, Norm?"

A. "No, but I am willing to add on."

B. "Terrorists have taken over my stomach and are demanding beer."

C. "Well, I am going to need something to kill time before my second beer. How about a first one?"

D. "It's not, but it doesn't mean that you can't."

E. "I never met a beer I didn't drink."

53. After Norm was forced to fire his secretary, she became infatuated with him and followed him everywhere. How did he solve the problem?

54. Vera gave Norm a membership to a health spa for his birthday. Norm said he did twenty-five of something in the pool each day. What?

55. Why did Norm get upset when Cliff decided to buy a condo and move out of Norm's house?

56. After Norm won some money gambling, what did he give Sam as credit toward his bar tab?

57. When Norm was audited by a female IRS agent and the audit began to go poorly, what did he do?

58. What did Cliff do to disrupt Norm and the IRS agent?
    A. He posed as Vera.
    B. He started a fire in the hotel.
    C. He released wild squirrels in the darkened hotel room.

59. When Norm got stuck in the back window of the bar, to what cartoon character did everyone compare him?

60. What was Norm's main concern when Sam considered hiring a new bar manager?

61. After narrowly escaping death when Robin's sailboat exploded, for what did Norm say he would have a greater appreciation?

62. How did Norm suffer an injury while sailing Robin's boat?
    A. He cut his thumb when the boat exploded.
    B. He cut his thumb on a beer bottle cap.
    C. He cut his thumb on the anchor.

63. When Frasier threatened to jump off the building above Cheers because Lilith had left him. Norm rushed outside. Why?
    A. To move his car
    B. To find Lilith
    C. To help Frasier

64. How did Norm acknowledge his fifteenth wedding anniversary to Vera?

Answers

1. George Wendt

2. Norm!

3. Norman!

4. C. Moonglow

5. Wrestling

6. B. Hungry Heifer

7. They were going on a hike.

8. Norm was the equipment manager.

9. The Coast Guard

10. A. Bora Bora

11. He hid in Sam's office.

12. B. "Never better, but just once I would like to be better."

13. A. "My ideal weight, if I was 11 feet tall."

14. E. "It's a dog-eat-dog world, and I'm wearing milk-bone underwear."

15. D. "Yes; now let's get Joe Beer nipping at my liver."

16. C. "Let's talk about what's going in Mr. Peterson."

17. A beer

18. He quit the company.

19. C. He bought the little painter's hat.

20. C. "My cheeks on this bar stool."

21. A. "Boy meets beer, boy drinks beer, boy gets another beer."

22. D. "Most of my wife."

23. E. "I don't know—I usually finish them before they get a word in."

24. B. "Just my usual: I'll have a trough of beer and a snorkel."

25. She offered him a free beer with every kitten.

26. Firing employees

27. Beer

28. C. "Funny, I was about to ask you the same thing."

29. D. "Elope with my wife."

30. E. "Beats me—I can't find the on-ramp."

31. B. "So float a cornflake in it."

32. A. "The warranty on my liver."

33. C. When he found out that Vera tricked him into marriage by telling him she was pregnant

34. An orangutan

35. B. "Thirsty guy walks into a bar; you finish it."

36. D. "How to sit. How to drink. Want to quiz me?"

37. E. "You really know how to make it sound tempting, you fast talker."

38. C. "A transfusion with a head on it."

39. A. "You mean nice cold beer going *down* Mr. Peterson."

40. D. All of the above

41. His bar tab

42. No

43. Women's undergarments

44. A. and B. Bif *and* Loobster

45. Paint the office

46. He invented a mean boss.

47. C. He had spilled it on the floor that morning.

48. D. "It's not, but it doesn't mean you can't."

49. E. "I never met a beer I didn't like."

50. A. "No, but I am willing to add on."

51. C. "Well, I am going to need something to kill time before my second beer. How about a first one?"

52. B. "Terrorists have taken over my stomach and are demanding beer."

53. He rehired her.

54. Cannonballs

55. Norm would be left to talk to Vera.

56. A sailboat

57. He flirted with the agent.

58. C. He released wild squirrels in the darkened hotel room.

59. Winnie-the-Pooh

60. If the price of beer would go up

61. Beer

62. B. He cut his thumb on a beer bottle cap.

63. A. To move his car

64. He waved to her from the bar as she drove by.

6

Cliff

Questions

1. Who played the part of Cliff Clavin?

2. For what government agency did Cliff proudly serve?

3. What part of Cliff's wardrobe was always predictably the same?

4. What was Cliff's middle initial?

5. Who played Cliff's mother?

6. What was Cliff's mother's character name?

7. What did Cliff call his mother?

8. How old did Cliff say he was when his mother cut off his allowance?
   A. 15
   B. 21
   C. 30

9. To what country's throne did Cliff claim to be an heir?

10. Why did Cliff collect phone books from every major metropolitan area in the country?

11. What bloodsucking worms did Cliff contend were a "medical cure-all"?

12. To prove that he was a black belt in karate, Cliff broke boards with his foot and his head. What did he do next?

13. What was Cliff excused from after giving an exhortation on why the guillotine should be used again?

14. Cliff was voted Postman of the Year, an award given to only 267 postmen in what area?
    A. The United States
    B. Massachusetts
    C. Greater Boston

15. What two catalogs did Cliff deliver on his route that caused him to walk hunched over?

16. On what "wall" did Carla claim Cliff's social calendar could be found?

17. At a costume party at the bar, Cliff and a woman became enchanted with each other. What characters were they dressed as?
    A. John Wayne and Mae West
    B. Paul Revere and Betsy Ross
    C. Ponce de León and Tinker Bell

18. On what did Cliff claim to be an expert?
    A. Tapeworms
    B. Snipes
    C. Beer

19. After Cliff got his mother hooked up with a millionaire named Fitz, what announcement upset Cliff?

    A. They were going to live together and not get married.

    B. They were going to live with Cliff.

    C. He was going to give his fortune to charity.

20. What happened at Fitz's bachelor's party that upset the wedding plans?

21. Cliff claimed that all athletic slumps could be categorized into four causes: physical, emotional, psychological, and what?

    A. Dental

    B. Financial

    C. Maternal

22. What animal did Cliff use to prove to Norm that it took little skill to paint?

23. After visiting Cliff, why did his father not stay in this country?

24. When Cliff grew a hybrid of a rutabaga and a beet, what snacks did he invent from it?

    A. Beetabaga Brittle

    B. Beetabaga Burritos

    C. Beetabaga Fajitas on Pita

    D. All of the above

25. What question from Norm prompted Cliff to give up writing a letter to a Russian cosmonaut stranded in a space station?

26. At the 100th anniversary party for the bar, what happened to Cliff after he introduced himself to the mayor as the postal worker who had written to him each year?

27. Cliff refused to leave his house when it was about to be leveled. What did he do to resist?

28. To which state did Ma Clavin move?

29. What was Cliff's favorite TV game show?

30. When Cliff went on *Jeopardy!* he did very well, since he was knowledgeable about most of the categories. Which of the following subjects was *not* a category?
    A. Civil Service
    B. Stamps From Around the World
    C. Bar Trivia
    D. They were all categories.

31. What happened to Cliff on the final *Jeopardy!* question?

32. The final *Jeopardy!* answer was: "Archibald Leach, Bernard Schwartz, and Lucille Le Sueur." What was Cliff's question?

33. What did Cliff talk Alex Trebek out of doing?

34. What feeling about Cliff did Alex Trebek and Norm share?

35. Why was Cliff hesitant to take his new girlfriend, Sally, out in public?

36. What did Sally do that motivated Cliff to take her out?

37. How did Cliff always address Frasier?

38. A new post office recruit was fired because she became personally involved with Cliff. She per-

suaded Cliff to run away to Canada with her. What song did the guys use to persuade Cliff to stay?
A. The *Jeopardy!* theme song
B. "America the Beautiful"
C. "Ballad of the Green Berets"

39. Cliff claimed that he received a love letter from a woman in Florida. What kind of letter was it really?

40. Why did Cliff claim that nobody ever messed with Switzerland?
    A. They all carry Swiss Army Knives.
    B. They have the highest per capita rate of postal workers.
    C. Everyone loves Swiss cheese.

41. At Rebecca's wedding we discover that the security guards at what government building consider Cliff a troublemaker?

42. According to Cliff, what part of the human anatomy would eventually disappear?

43. Cliff's mother unexpectedly visited from Florida because she owed money to certain people for a race on which she bet. What type of race?

44. When Ma Clavin stayed with Woody, what type of trivia did she teach him?

45. Cliff claimed he could never have low self-esteem because he had something that was eight percent larger than that of most humans. What was it?
    A. Head
    B. Feet
    C. Cerebral Cortex

46. What former would-be world leader did Cliff believe lived in his apartment building?

47. What did Cliff claim he always sent to women when he broke their hearts?
    A. Flowers
    B. A box of candy
    C. A box of dried figs

48. How did Cliff claim he was going to preserve himself forever?

49. What publication printed one of Cliff's jokes?

50. Cliff tried to sell a joke to Johnny Carson and it was refused. Who altered the rejection letter to look as if the joke was accepted?

51. How did Cliff's joke finally get into Johnny's monologue?

52. Who ended up sitting on stage with Johnny?

53. Complete Cliff's joke for Johnny. "Doc Severinsen is so old, when he was a kid he never blew out candles on his birthday cake, because they didn't have _____ yet."

54. Which of the following publications did Cliff read?
    A. *True Stories of UFOs*
    B. *The History of UFOs*
    C. *UFO Spotter's Guide*

55. While in the hospital for minor surgery, Cliff did not have any visitors and realized that no one liked him because he was too obnoxious. By what method did he try to change his behavior?

   A. Electric stimulus

   B. Counseling

   C. Buying drinks for everyone

56. When Cliff was hired to videotape a fiftieth wedding anniversary, his camera battery died. What did he do?

57. Which of the following events—all of which seemed unimportant to Cliff anyway—was he unable to tape?

   A. Father told kids that he loved them.

   B. Marine son returned from duty.

   C. Mother stood and walked from wheelchair.

   D. All of the above

58. What was Cliff's suggestion to Frasier to keep Lilith from leaving him?

59. What did Cliff's friends do to help him get accepted into an experimental underground city?

60. Cliff fainted at the prospect of becoming a father. While Carla tried to revive him by splashing water on his face, something fell on his head. What?

Answers

1. John Ratzenberger

2. U.S. Postal Service

3. His socks were always white.

4. C.

5. Frances Sternhagen

6. Esther Clavin

7. Ma

8. C. 30

9. Russia's

10. He collected phone book cover art.

11. Leeches

12. He asked Diane to take him to the hospital.

13. Jury duty

14. C. Greater Boston

15. Sears and Spiegel

16. The men's room wall

17. C. Ponce de León and Tinker Bell

18. A. Tapeworms

19. C. He was going to give his fortune to charity.

20. Fitz died.

21. A. Dental

22. An orangutan

23. He was wanted for real estate fraud.

24. D. All of the above

25. "How are you going to send it to him?"

26. He was arrested.

27. He handcuffed himself inside the house.

28. Florida

29. *Jeopardy!*

30. D. They were all categories.

31. He bet all of his winnings and lost.

32. "Who are three people who have never been in my kitchen?" (The correct question: "Who are Cary Grant, Tony Curtis, and Joan Crawford?")

33. Resigning from *Jeopardy!*

34. That Cliff scared them

35. She was plain-looking.

36. She made herself look gorgeous.

37. Doc

38. C. "Ballad of the Green Berets"

39. A demand that he return all of the towels and ash-trays that he had taken from the motel

40. A. They all carry Swiss Army Knives.

41. City Hall

42. The little finger

43. A dog race

44. Bird trivia

45. C. Cerebral cortex

46. Hitler

47. C. A box of dried figs

48. Cryogenics—to freeze and preserve his brain

49. *The Postal Newsletter*

50. Norm

51. Norm bribed the cue-card man.

52. Ma Clavin

53. Fire

54. C. *UFO Spotter's Guide*

55. A. Electric stimulus

56. He pretended to tape the remainder of the event.

57. D. All of the above

58. Fake a heart attack.

59. They started a petition to get him accepted.

60. The toilet lid

7

Carla

Questions

1. Who played the part of Carla?

2. Which one of the following was *not* part of Carla's full name?
   A. Carla
   B. Maria
   C. Victoria
   D. Angelina
   E. Teresa
   F. Madonna
   G. Adollonia
   H. Lozupone
   I. Tortelli
   J. LeBec

3. Carla and Diane shared a childhood nickname. What was it?
   A. Muffin
   B. Trixie
   C. Precious

4. Which of the following was *not* one of the names of Carla's children?

A. Anthony
B. Gino
C. Ann Marie
D. Nick
E. Serafina
F. Lucinda
G. Ludlow
H. Elvis
I. Jessie

5. What qualification did Carla feel she had that proved she was congenial, and therefore qualified to be in the Miss Boston Barmaid Contest?

6. During one of Carla's maternity leaves, her "wallflower" sister helped out in the bar. Who played Carla's sister?

7. Whenever Carla was pregnant, she always felt labor pains and needed to leave the bar when a certain basketball team was playing. What team?

8. What was Carla's favorite meal?
   A. Steak
   B. Chicken McNuggets
   C. Spaghetti

9. When Carla's high school principal (whom Carla despised) showed up at the bar, what did Carla want to do to her?
   A. Shave her head
   B. Pour beer on her
   C. Put a tattoo on her

10. What did Carla eventually do to the principal?

The on-going battle between Carla and Diane is temporarily
put aside when Carla's ex-husband takes custody of her oldest
son and Diane is determined to help her get him back.
(*AP/Wide World Photos*)

11. When the gang started to watch a TV news report about a woman on the ledge of a building, Carla asked for the rest of the day off. Why?

12. Who played Carla's ex-husband, Nick Tortelli?

13. Which of the following things did Carla love about Nick?
    A. The way he flexed his tattoo
    B. The way hair grew in his ears
    C. The way he drooled while asleep
    D. All of the above

14. What kind of school did Carla pay for Nick to attend?

15. Who played Nick Tortelli's new bride?

16. What photos did Nick send with his wedding invitations?

17. How did Loretta always address the gang at Cheers?

18. After Carla entered a barmaid contest she came to suspect that Cliff was one of the judges. What did she do?

19. Carla did not win the contest, but she did win an award. What was it?
    A. Fastest
    B. Most accurate
    C. Most congenial

20. When Carla questioned her belief in God, what "sign from God" made her believe again?
    A. Diane announced she was leaving.
    B. Cliff split his pants.
    C. Norm turned down a beer.

21. Why did Carla's family like to watch *America's Most Wanted?*

22. When Nick returned with Loretta, what did they want Carla to give to them?

23. Loretta left Nick (temporarily) to join a touring singing group. What was it called?
    A. The Smiling Americans
    B. The Grinning Americans
    C. The Toothy Americans

24. When Nick thought that Sam was after Loretta, what did Nick do to get revenge?

25. When Nick tried to hypnotize Diane, who was hypnotized instead?

26. Starting with his lucky quarter, Carla's grandfather amassed a fortune. The fortune was then squandered by one of his heirs. What was left for Carla?

27. As teenagers, Carla and Nick were members of a local TV dance show. What was the name of the show?
    A. *The Boston Boppers*
    B. *The Boston Poppers*
    C. *The Boston Toppers*

28. To whom did Sam compare Carla and Nick's dancing?
    A. Fred and Ginger
    B. Fred and Ethel
    C. Fred and Barney

29. Carla fell in love with Eddie LeBec, who played what sport?

30. What disc jockey and actor played Eddie LeBec?

31. For what team did Eddie play?

32. After Carla and Eddie began to date, he began to slump. What did Carla conclude was the problem?

33. What did Carla do to improve Eddie's game?

34. What was Carla and Eddie's song?
    A. The Canadian National Anthem
    B. "Hound Dog"
    C. "Muskrat Love"

35. Who did not want Carla and Eddie to get married?

36. What made Carla and Eddie think they should not get married?

37. What type of job did Eddie get when he could not continue in hockey?

38. Why did Carla not want to visit Eddie when he was away?

39. Carla inherited $50,000 from Eddie's life insurance policy. What did Carla offer the guys so that they would keep it quiet from Eddie's other widow?

40. What singer did Carla hope would come back to life on his birthday?

41. Carla was very pleased that Serafina's husband-to-be had a steady income. What was the income from?

42. Who provided the music at Serafina's wedding?
    A. Commander Collins and the Road Rockers

B. Captain Gus and the Polka Pirates

C. Sergeant Steve and the Jazz Jets

43. What wedding gift did Ma Clavin give to Norm and Vera, who gave it to Frasier and Lilith, who gave it to Woody and Kelly, who gave it to Serafina and Patrick?

    A. *Brady Bunch* Blender

    B. *Father Knows Best* Toaster

    C. *Star Trek* Steak Knives

44. What wedding gift did Nick and Loretta give Serafina?

45. For what type of animal act did Nick try to get investors?

46. Carla's mother requested that Carla carry on a family tradition by changing the name of one of her sons. What name did her mother request?

47. When Carla was depressed about becoming a grandmother, what did the girls do to remind her of her youth?

48. What happened to Cliff that brought Carla out of her depression?

    A. He ripped his pants.

    B. She "pantsed" him.

    C. He was hit with a pie.

49. Carla was very disappointed when Elvis failed to appear on his birthday. Who put on an Elvis wig and sent her flowers?

50. What did Carla say to Hill that she believed caused his heart attack?

51. What did Carla think she would be guaranteed after her son said he wanted to be a priest?

52. After Carla had mocked God by playing tricks on everyone, her son decided he did not want to be a priest. What did Carla do to repent?

Answers

1. Rhea Perlman

2. F. Madonna

3. A. Muffin

4. D. Nick

5. She was pregnant.

6. Rhea Perlman

7. The Boston Celtics

8. B. Chicken McNuggets

9. A. Shave her head

10. She shaved half of her head.

11. The women was her kids' baby-sitter.

12. Dan Hedaya

13. D. All of the above

14. TV repair school

15. Jean Kasem (wife of disc jockey Casey Kasem)

16. Pictures of him and Loretta in the buff

17. "Gang at Cheers"

18. She was nice to him.

19. C. Most Congenial

20. A. Diane announced she was leaving.

21. To rat on their neighbors

22. One of Carla's children

23. B. The Grinning Americans

24. He went after Diane.

25. Woody

26. Her grandfather's lucky quarter

27. A. *The Boston Boppers*

28. B. Fred and Ethel

29. Ice hockey

30. Jay Thomas

31. The Boston Bruins

32. She was jinxing his game.

33. She broke up with him.

34. A. The Canadian National Anthem

35. Eddie's mother

36. Their superstitions

37. He dressed as a penguin in an ice show.

38. She was afraid to fly.

39. Free beer

40. Elvis Presley

41. Disability payments from the Police Department

42. B. Captain Gus and the Polka Pirates

43. C. *Star Trek* Steak Knives

44. *Star Trek* Steak Knives

45. An orangutan act

46. Benito Mussolini

47. They had a slumber party.

48. A. He ripped his pants.

49. John Allen Hill, the new owner of Melville's

50. "I love you."

51. Automatic entry into heaven

52. She listened to Cliff practice his comedy act.

8

Woody

Questions

1. Who played the part of Woody Boyd?

2. What city and state was Woody from?

3. What was his hometown known as?
   A. The shoehorn capital of the world
   B. The place mat capital of the world
   C. The lampshade capital of the world

4. What was Woody's middle name?

5. Whom did Woody come to Cheers to meet?

6. Woody said he did some fast talking to get a good lease on his apartment. How long was his lease?
   A. Month to month
   B. One year
   C. Ten years

7. Woody compared the Rose Parade to what parade in Hanover, Indiana?

8. What was the name of Woody's girlfriend from back home?

9. To keep their minds off sex, what did Woody and his girlfriend do instead?

10. When Woody needed a date to impress his ex-girlfriend, whom did he end up with?
   A. Diane
   B. An escort-service woman
   C. Sam's cleaning woman

11. Woody proudly told the story of the time he ran for class president, but was elected to a different position instead. What?

12. What did Woody claim would happen when a turkey ate too much and began to hiss?

13. To whom did Woody claim he passed notes in school?
   A. His cousin
   B. His brother
   C. His father

14. How did Woody get to be Employee-of-the-Month for four consecutive months?

15. What did Woody keep in his shoe to help him retrieve his life savings?
   A. A map to where it was buried
   B. A combination to a safe
   C. A key to a safety-deposit box

16. Woody wanted to bet his savings on a football game, but in an effort to protect him, Sam never placed the bet. Woody would have won. What did Woody want from Sam to make up for the loss of winnings?

17. Who was on the line when Woody called a "900 party line"?

18. Woody said that wearing a uniform to the bar saved him a couple of hours each day. How?

19. What was Woody's mother's dream?
    A. To visit Chicago
    B. To work at the local feed store
    C. To be a drummer in a hard-rock band

20. What did Woody do to animals back home during a bachelor party?

21. When the corporate office forced Woody to go on a vacation, he missed his flight to Italy. Where did he enjoy spending the week?

22. In what real TV show, filmed in Boston, did Woody claim he appeared?

23. Woody made a TV commercial for a vegetable and fruit drink in which his line was: "I like it." But, what problem did Woody later discover?

24. What was the name of the drink that Woody endorsed?
    A. Veggie Fruits
    B. Fruity Boy
    C. Veggie Boy

25. What did Frasier do to help Woody like the drink?

26. After Woody came to like the drink, what was his problem?

27. Would-be actor Woody was an understudy for the

part of a famous author. While dressed for the part, he made quite an impression on an elderly woman. What author did he portray?

28. While tending bar at the Gaines estate, Woody met Kelly Gaines and inadvertently offended her boyfriend, Nash. How did Nash get his revenge?

29. In what sport did Nash participate at Princeton?

30. How did Woody get back at Nash?

31. Who played the part of Kelly?

32. Woody laughed uncontrollably when he read what comic strip?
    A. Ziggy
    B. *Peanuts*
    C. *Garfield*

33. When a woman biker came into the bar, Woody told her that he once belonged to a biker gang. What kind of bike did Woody say he had?

34. Why did Woody say he did not want to be rich?
    A. He was afraid he would become greedy.
    B. He did not want to carry all of his money around with him.
    C. He would have to memorize the serial numbers on all of his money.

35. Since Woody could not afford an expensive birthday gift for Kelly, he wrote and sang her a song. What word was excessively repeated throughout the song?

36. What did Kelly have over a thousand of in her bedroom?

    A. Dresses
    B. Hairbrushes
    C. Barbie dolls

37. Whom did Sam suggest visit Kelly's room?

38. Before Kelly went to Europe, she and Woody agreed to keep something secret. What?

39. When Kelly returned from her studies in Europe, she brought Henri with her. What did he always tease Woody about?

40. Who played Henri?

41. In what way did Henri propose to legally stay in this country?

42. When Kelly was trying to fit into Woody's "world," what mode of transportation had she never heard of?

43. When Kelly worked in the bar for a day, what did Carla tell her tips were?

44. What did Norm tell Kelly to do with his bar tab every time he had one beer?

45. Woody tried to negotiate a $100-per-month raise. When Sam objected, Woody made a counteroffer which Sam gladly accepted. How much was the raise?
    A. $1 per day
    B. $30 per week
    C. $1,000 per year

46. When Rebecca asked Woody to iron her clothes, he did not realize that the iron had a spray setting. What did he use for water on her clothes?

47. What did Woody keep back home in the barn to keep the cats away?

48. Prior to meeting Kelly's mother, why did Woody say she was his last hope?

49. What did Kelly's mother do to Woody at a family party?

50. To help pay for Kelly's engagement ring, Woody got a second job on a graveyard shift. Where?

51. When Woody met Kelly's grandmother, he was deathly afraid of her. Why?

52. After Woody told Rebecca about all of his various charity work, Rebecca felt so guilty she wanted to kill herself. What did Woody give her?

53. Based on her astrological analysis, what did Carla predict would happen if Woody and Kelly were married on their planned wedding day?

54. At the wedding, what did Mr. Gaines do when his family met Woody's family?

55. Why did Woody's Uncle Elroy need a plunger just because he wanted to dance?

56. Which of the following events did *not* happen at Woody's wedding?
    A. The first minister died.
    B. The second minister got drunk.
    C. The chefs left.
    D. Lilith played the spoons to entertain the guests.
    E. Rebecca ate the head off the groom figurine.

F. The corpse fell on the cake.

G. All of the above happened.

57. How did Woody manage to sleep through a classical concert without being discovered?

58. On what cable channel did Woody get hooked?

59. Woody and Kelly thought their marriage was doomed when they discovered that they were of different religions. What two religions?
    A. Jewish and Baptist
    B. Catholic and Methodist
    C. Lutheran Church of America and Lutheran Church of Missouri Synod

60. Woody tried to invent a new cocktail. What problem did he encounter when he finally came up with a good one?

61. Why did Woody say his theater group had to be twice as furious when doing the play *Twelve Angry Men*?

Answers

1. Woody Harrelson

2. Hanover, Indiana

3. B. The place mat capital of the world

4. Tiberius

5. Coach

6. C. Ten years

7. The Corn Parade

8. Beth

9. They ate incessantly.

10. C. Sam's cleaning woman

11. Class clown

12. It would explode.

13. C. His father

14. No one else wanted it.

15. A. A map to where it was buried

16. Sam's Corvette

17. Cliff

18. He no longer had to take the time to choose a shirt.

19. C. To be a drummer in a hard-rock band

20. Dressed them in women's clothing

21. In the airport

22. *Spenser For Hire*

23. He did not like it.

24. C. Veggie Boy

25. He hypnotized Woody.

26. He became addicted to it.

27. Mark Twain

28. He beat up Woody.

29. Boxing

30. Woody took Kelly on a date.

31. Jackie Swanson

32. A. Ziggy

33. A Schwinn

34. C. He would have to memorize the serial numbers on all of his money.

35. "Kelly"

36. C. Barbie dolls

37. G.I. Joe

38. Their engagement

39. Stealing Kelly from Woody

40. Anthony Cistaro

41. By marrying Kelly

42. The subway

43. Monetary gifts for the head waitress (Carla)

44. Erase one beer from his tab

45. B. $30 per week

46. Spit

47. Rats

48. Nobody else in the family liked Woody.

49. She flirted with him.

50. At a graveyard

51. He thought he had seen her as a corpse at the graveyard.

52. The phone number of the suicide-prevention hot line at which he also volunteered

53. The wedding would be a disaster.

54. Mr. Gaines immediately opened the bar.

55. Uncle Elroy left his leg on the bus.

56. G. All of the above happened.

57. He placed fake eyeballs over his eyes.

58. *Home Shopping Network*

59. C. Lutheran Church of America and Lutheran Church of Missouri Synod

60. He could not remember the ingredients.

61. The troupe had only six actors.

9

Frasier and Lilith

Questions

1. Who played the part of Frasier Crane?

2. What was Frasier's occupation?

3. Who was Frasier's patient when he was introduced in the series?

4. What happened to Frasier at his first hockey game?

5. Frasier took Carla and other patients on an airplane flight to conquer their fear of flying. What happened?

6. Who played the part of Lilith?

7. How did Diane help Frasier and Lilith's relationship to blossom?

8. Where were Frasier and Lilith when they began to be attracted to each other?

9. Just prior to Frasier and Lilith's wedding, Cliff convinced Frasier that another woman was interested in him. Who?

10. Prior to his bachelor party, Lilith gave Frasier the chance to do something. What?

11. How did Frasier already know the stripper at his bachelor party?

12. After getting drunk at her bachelorette party, what did Lilith wish to be called?
    A. Sheena, Queen of the Jungle of Love
    B. Sheeba, Queen of the Amazons
    C. Sheema, Queen of Boston

13. What convinced Frasier that he loved Lilith and wanted to marry her?

14. When Frasier decided to diet and exercise, who became his personal trainer?

15. Frasier and Cliff argued over whether women are drawn to married men. To prove Cliff wrong, Frasier tried to flirt with two beautiful women. What happened?

16. After firing a famous interior decorator, whom did Frasier and Lilith hire to redecorate their home?

17. What did Frasier say was the main advantage of a psychiatrist over a psychic?

18. Sam and Cliff made a bet as to how long Frasier would last during acupuncture. Who else wanted in on the bet?

19. While trying to start a fire in the country, Frasier asked Lilith to sing a work song to help his rhythm. Lilith sang the only song she knew. What was it?
    A. "I've Been Working on the Railroad"
    B. "Oklahoma"
    C. "My Funny Valentine"

Dr. Frasier Crane (Kelsey Grammer) checks the new family addition that his wife, Dr. Lilith Stenin-Crane (Bebe Neuwrith), is expecting. (*AP/Wide World Photos*)

20. Frasier told the guys that Lilith had taught him to control his body in an effort to pretend to be dead. When did she teach this to Frasier?
    A. On their honeymoon
    B. On their wedding day
    C. The first time his mother visited

21. Lilith gave Frasier a "provocative" photo of herself on a bearskin rug. What was she wearing?

22. What was the name of Frasier and Lilith's son?

23. When Frasier needed advice on how to be a clown, what did Woody tell him?
    A. "Fall down a lot."
    B. "Use a trick handkerchief."
    C. "Be yourself."

24. Frasier's clown suit had a trick handkerchief; when it was pulled the pants would drop, revealing funny underwear. What problem did Frasier have with this?

25. What did Lilith do to win the First Annual Tricks With Digits Exposition?
    A. She put her fist in her mouth.
    B. She cracked her knuckles.
    C. She snapped her fingers to the *William Tell* Overture.

26. After Frasier's Low Self-Esteem Group heard that his Dysfunctional Men's Group had gone to Cheers for a session, how did the members of the Low Self-Esteem Group feel?

27. What suggestion from Norm did the Low Self-Esteem Group carry out against Frasier?

28. Why did Lilith purchase an evening with Sam at a charity auction?

29. Which of the following events did *not* take place at Frederick's bris in the bar?
    A. A retirement party
    B. A wet T-shirt contest
    C. A funeral
    D. All of the above happened.

30. While Lilith was away, Frasier cared for one of her laboratory rats. What was the rat's name?
    A. Frasier
    B. Mickey
    C. Whiskers

31. While Frasier was taking care of Lilith's rat, what happened to it?

32. When Lilith appeared on a TV talk show to discuss her new book, *Good Girls, Bad Boys,* Frasier joined her onstage as an example of a good boy. Who went on stage as a bad boy?

33. What did Lilith's mother insist that Frasier and Lilith do on their fifth wedding anniversary?

34. After Frederick spent the day at Cheers, he spoke his first word. What was it?

35. When the Cranes had Frederick's development tested, they were quite distressed at the results. What was Frederick's rating?

36. What did Frasier do to keep from laughing at Lilith's new hairstyle?

    A. He attached a mousetrap to his finger.

    B. He bit his lip.

    C. He slammed his hand in a drawer.

37. Frasier and Lilith took Frederick to see a famous children's entertainer, Nanny Gee. During the performance, Frasier realized that he knew Nanny Gee. How did he know her?

38. Nanny Gee gave Frederick a singing doll for his birthday. What did the doll continually repeat?

39. What was the name of Lilith's laboratory rat that died?

    A. Whitey

    B. Blackie

    C. Frasier

40. When Lilith had trouble dealing with the rat's death, she carried it around with her. In what?

41. What child actors played Frederick?

42. What did Lilith say would be tax-deductible when she published her book on "borderline psychosis"?

43. When Lilith left Frasier she went on a scientific experiment. Where?

44. What did Frasier think would happen to him if he visited Woody's hometown?

    A. He'd become a farmer's breeding stud.

    B. He'd be forced to marry an ugly farm girl.

    C. He'd become a human sacrifice to the "Corn God."

Answers

1. Kelsey Grammer

2. Psychiatrist

3. Diane

4. He was arrested for fighting.

5. Frasier lost his nerve.

6. Bebe Neuwirth

7. She made Lilith look more attractive.

8. On a television psychology show

9. Rebecca

10. Back out of the wedding

11. She was his patient.

12. A. Sheena, Queen of the Jungle of Love

13. He became jealous.

14. Sam

15. Lilith walked in.

16. Norm

17. A psychiatrist can prescribe drugs.

18. Lilith

19. C. "My Funny Valentine"

20. A. On their honeymoon

21. A business suit

22. Frederick

23. C. "Be yourself."

24. He wasn't wearing any underwear.

25. A. She put her fist in her mouth.

26. They did not feel good enough to go.

27. They "pantsed" him.

28. To make Frasier jealous

29. C. A funeral

30. C. Whiskers

31. It got out of its cage.

32. Sam

33. Renew their wedding vows

34. Norm!

35. Average

36. A. He attached a mousetrap to his finger.

37. She was Frasier's first wife.

38. Nanny Gee's telephone number

39. A. Whitey

40. Her purse

41. Christopher and Kevin Graves

42. All of the money she had spent at Cheers

43. She went to live in an experimental underground city.

44. C. He'd become a human sacrifice to the "Corn God."

10

Rebecca

Questions

1. Who played the part of Rebecca Howe?

2. What was Rebecca's occupation when she began on the show?

3. Where did Rebecca say her dream job would be?
   A. IBM
   B. Disneyland
   C. International House of Pancakes

4. What was Rebecca's nickname in college?

5. After kissing Sam, in which of the following categories did Rebecca place him?
   A. Yes
   B. No
   C. Definite maybe

6. Sam made a date with Rebecca's sister, so that Rebecca would do what?

7. What did Rebecca do when she caught Sam and her sister kissing?

8. Where did Rebecca try to hide a lit cigarette when she was trying to conceal her smoking habit from Sam?

9. Rebecca was very interested in one of the executives with her company, Evan Drake. What Emmy award-winning actor played Evan?

10. When Sam and Rebecca shared a stateroom on Evan's yacht, Sam pretended to be asleep while he put his arm around Rebecca. What did Rebecca do to his hand?
    A. She kissed it.
    B. She tattooed it.
    C. She slammed it in the nightstand drawer.

11. Evan sent a substitute waitress to work at Cheers. Rebecca thought that she was Evan's mistress and hit her. What was her relationship to Evan?

12. While Norm was painting Evan's house, he let Rebecca in to look around. When Evan returned unexpectedly, where did Rebecca hide?

13. Rebecca was able to sneak out of Evan's house, when Norm persuaded Evan to help him fulfill a childhood fantasy. What did the fantasy involve?
    A. Having an Easter egg hunt with a rich guy on a lawn
    B. Carrying a rich guy across a lawn
    C. Playing croquet with a rich guy on a lawn

14. When Rebecca could not find a pair of diamond earrings, which of the following chairmen of the

Joint Chiefs of Staff did she suspect took them?
A. General Alexander Haig
B. Admiral William J. Crowe, Jr.
C. General Colin Powell

15. Rebecca's business school professor visited her at Cheers. Rebecca presented her with a rewritten term paper. What was the title of the paper?
A. "Jimmy Carter—The Three-Term President"
B. "Buy High and Sell Low"
C. "How to Succeed in Business Without Really Trying"

16. Robin Colcord first visited Cheers when he came to thank Rebecca for her letters giving him real estate suggestions. What else had she included with the letters?

17. Who played the part of Robin Colcord?

18. What nickname did Rebecca have for Robin?

19. Robin gave Rebecca a bracelet with a replica of one of his buildings. What were the windows made of?

20. Before Sam could tell Rebecca that he cared for her, someone beat him to it. Who?

21. Robin gave Rebecca an antique desk and seemed to imply that there was a ring hidden inside of it. As it turned out, the desk was a valuable antique known as the "Ring Desk." What did Rebecca do to the desk?

22. What trapped Sam and Rebecca in Robin's penthouse?

23. Sam and Robin played chess for a week's worth of the other's salary, and Sam won. Since Robin was legally incorporated, what was his weekly salary after taxes?

24. Rebecca went on a "consumer complaint" TV show to complain about a women's razor. As it turned out, who owned the razor company?

25. After Robin told Rebecca that he loved her, he showed up with another woman at the same restaurant where Rebecca was. How did Sam get Rebecca out of the restaurant without her seeing Robin?

26. What did Robin offer Sam in exchange for his silence about Robin's other girlfriend?

27. Who hosted Rebecca's bachelorette party?

28 What did Rebecca begin to doubt at her bachelorette party?

29. Where did Rebecca and Robin have their wedding?

30. Who sang at Rebecca and Robin's wedding?

31. What did Rebecca call the singer?

32. What song did he sing?
    A. *"Unchained Melody"*
    B. *"You've Lost That Loving Feeling"*
    C. *"I've got the Wedding Bell Blues"*

33. When Rebecca realized that she was only marrying Robin for his money, which he no longer had, she

called off the wedding. What did Robin return to Cheers to retrieve?

34. After Rebecca left Robin at the altar, where did she go to get her life back together?

35. After getting herself together, Rebecca realized that there was something she needed to do to regain her self-esteem. What?
   A. She wanted to marry Sam.
   B. She wanted to have Sam's baby.
   C. She wanted to own the bar.

36. After Rebecca lost her job at the bar, she claimed that she got a job in public relations. What was her job?

37. In her public relations job, which of the following was Rebecca supposed to demonstrate on the car?
   A. Acid
   B. Fire
   C. Boiling Tar
   D. All of the above

38. After Rebecca bought back the poolroom from John Allen Hill, who owned Melville's, what did she do with it?

39. What type of food did Rebecca eventually serve in the converted poolroom?

40. After Sam finally acknowledged that Rebecca had made a success of the converted poolroom, he helped himself to some of her food. What happened?
   A. The pressure cooker blew up.

B. He got food poisoning.

C. He broke a tooth.

41. What did Rebecca claim she would have tattooed on her if Sam gained a high bid at a celebrity auction?

Answers

1. Kirstie Alley

2. She was the new bar manager.

3. C. International House of Pancakes

4. Backseat Becky

5. C. Definite maybe

6. Be jealous and go out with Sam

7. She pretended to shoot her (to trick Sam).

8. In her mouth

9. Tom Skerritt

10. C. She slammed it in the nightstand drawer.

11. She was his daughter.

12. In his bedroom closet

13. B. Carrying a rich guy across a lawn

14. B. Admiral William J. Crowe, Jr.

15. A. "Jimmy Carter—The Three-Term President"

16. Pictures of herself

17. Roger Rees

18. Sweet Baby

19. Diamonds

20. Robin

21. She destroyed it looking for the ring.

22. A laser-beam security system

23. $0.01

24. Robin Colcord

35. Sam told her the restaurant was on fire, covered her head with his jacket, and led her out.

26. He offered to buy back the bar for Sam.

27. Lilith

28. She began to doubt her love for Robin.

29. City Hall

30. Bobbie Hatfield

31. "The Other Righteous Brother"

32. A. *"Unchained Melody"*

33. A hidden money belt

34. Home to San Diego

35. C. She wanted to own the bar.

36. A model at a car show

37. D. All of the above

38. Turned it into a tearoom

39. Chili

40. A. The pressure cooker blew up.

41. Sam's name

11

The Later Years

Questions

1. After Diane did not return to Sam, he sold the bar to a big corporation. Where did he then go?

2. After Diane failed to write her novel, where did she go?

3. Why did Sam return to Cheers?

4. Sam made a date with one of Frasier's patients, whom he believed was obsessed with male dancers. His date turned out to be a different patient, who suffered from what?

5. After the guys complained of the lack of life's challenges, they were talked into doing what?

6. Why did Sam do it?

7. Why did Cliff finally jump?

8. Sam and Woody made a bet to see who could kiss Rebecca first. What went wrong when Sam pretended to choke and need mouth-to-mouth resuscitation?

9. What went wrong when Woody tried to hypnotize Rebecca in an effort to kiss her?

10. What did Rebecca trick Sam and Woody into doing in her darkened office under the guise of kissing her?

Mickey Mouse disappeared before his sixtieth birthday on "Mickey's 60th Birthday" which premiered on *The Magical World of Disney*, and wandered into the Cheers bar and sang "Happy Birthday" to Rebecca (Kirstie Alley). © 1988 The Walt Disney Company (*AP/Wide World Photos*)

11. After the"kiss" was over, what did Woody ask Sam?

12. Which of the following happened when the gang celebrated the bar's 100th anniversary?
    A. The mayor had Cliff arrested.
    B. Lilith went into labor.
    C. The 106-year-old guest of honor faked a heart attack to try to get girls.
    D. All of the above

13. Robin Colcord asked Sam to sail his yacht in a race, since he was unable to, due to his involvement in delicate union negotiations. What did Sam find on the yacht during the race?

14. After Sam exposed Robin for insider trading, the corporation was so grateful that it offered to sell the bar back to Sam. Sam had to borrow money to close the deal. How much did the corporation ask for the bar?

15. One person became jealous of the trivia napkins that Sam introduced at the bar. Who?

16. Where did Sam end up when he baby-sat the Cranes' son?

17. What did Sam decide after Frasier told him that he was spending too much time with Frederick and interfering with the family?

18. Who convinced Sam that Rebecca would be a good mother?

19. Before having a child, Sam and Rebecca decided to test themselves as parents by baby-sitting Carla's kids. Before they began, Carla insisted that they sign a form. What type of form?

20. Why did Sam and Rebecca decide not to have a baby together?

21. Who played the part of Phil?

22. With whom did Woody's cousin, Russell, fall in love?

23. What did Russell paint on his motel bedroom wall?

24. When Sam offered group medical insurance to his employees, he needed to add one more person so that everyone would qualify. Whom did he add?

25. When Cliff and Norm claimed that living their lives vicariously through Sam had become boring, whom did they consider using next?
    A. Phil
    B. Frasier
    C. Woody

26. While on vacation, Woody sent postcards to the gang. Each card said the same thing, with one exception. Whose card did not say, "I miss you most of all"?

27. Who played John Allen Hill, the new owner of Melville's?

28. While looking at his property deed, Hill discovered that he owned what part of Cheers?

29. Who won the betting pool on when Hill would make Sam go crazy?

30. What did Sam take from Hill to get even with him for taking part of Sam's bar?
    A. His waitress
    B. A doormat
    C. His parking space

31. Which of the following did Hill offer to Sam in exchange for Sam's agreement not to date his daughter?
    A. Free rent on his poolroom and rest rooms
    B. Use of Hill's parking space
    C. Free hairstyling

32. When Cliff tried to be a stand-up comedian, who was the only one who found his jokes humorous?

33. What bar regular did Norm and Cliff claim was originally a trained athlete who came to the bar to help them exercise?

34. Whom did Carla get to help free Frasier's hand from what Carla considered to be a cursed Foosball table?

35. After Sam was promoted to an executive position at the corporate office, he found out that he was being used as a "ringer." For what?

36. When something was stolen from Sam, he started a support group with others in the same situation. What was stolen?

37. While cutting Sam's hair, what did Woody get caught in Sam's hair which he then had to cut out?

38. To challenge the cold winter weather, Paul suggested that the other guys do what he did when he was growing up: jump into the ocean. Where did Paul grow up?

39. Who played the part of Paul?

40. The guys went on a trip together to get in touch with their true primal instincts, a theory which Fraiser called:

    A. The Inner Hairy Man

    B. The Beast Within

    C. The Macho Man

41. While on the trip, the guys became stranded in the desert and Norm wandered off by himself. Where did Norm spend the night?

42. Norm and Cliff felt bad about not including Paul in their activities, so they brought him a pizza and a cake. What did they decide to do while they waited for Paul to arrive at the bar?

43. After taking a fertility test, Sam was unable to look at the results. Carla decided to burn them, but burned something else instead. What?

Answers

1. He tried to sail around the world.

2. She went to Hollywood to write for television.

3. His boat sank.

4. Pyromania

5. Going skydiving

6. To impress Rebecca

7. He was tricked into thinking the plane was crashing.

8. Al, a crusty, old, bar regular, offered to give it to Sam.

9. He hypnotized himself.

10. Kissing each other

11. Woody asked Sam how well he thought he kissed.

12. D. All of the above

13. A bomb intended for Robin

14. $1.00

15. Cliff

16. Sam locked himself outside the second-floor window.

17. Sam decided to have his own child.

18. Elvis Presley

19. A liability release form

20. They did not love each other.

21. Phil Perlman (Rhea's father)

22. Rebecca

23. A portrait of Rebecca

24. Norm

25. A. Phil

26. Cliff's

27. Keene Curtis

28. The bathrooms and poolroom

29. Hill

30. B. A doormat

31. A. and B. Free rent on his poolroom and rest rooms *and* use of Hill's parking space

32. Lilith

33. Paul

34. A priest

35. The corporate softball team

36. His Corvette

37. His gum

38. Honolulu

39. Paul Willson

40. A. The Inner Hairy Man

42. At the resort on the other side of the hill

42. They ate the pizza and the cake.

43. Frasier's will

12

Bar Wars: The Practical Jokes

Questions

1. When Diane was asked to recite one of her poems on a public TV show, she thought the gang was trying to trick her. What did she do instead?

2. What was the name of the bar with which Cheers competed at sports and practical jokes?

3. Who played Gary of the rival bar?

4. At what sport did Carla think Cheers could beat Gary's, because it could be played by out-of-shape couch potatoes who sat around and drank beer all day?

5. What was the only sport at which Cheers beat Gary's?

6. Who was instrumental in helping the gang beat Gary's?

7. What did the guys do when they took Frasier on a "snipe hunt"?

8. What did Frasier plan to do when he went on the second snipe hunt?

9. Woody adjusted a target on the sidewalk while Norm and Cliff tried to hit it with water balloons from a skyscraper window. Where did the balloons continually land?

10. At what type of drink competition did Cheers and Gary's compete?

11. When Cheers gave the patrons of Gary's bar champagne as a peace offering, what was the joke?

12. What did Gary do to the bar stools at Cheers?

13. What kind of animal did Gary put in Rebecca's office?

14. When Woody tried to spy on Gary's, what did he dress as that gave him away?

15. When the gang thought that Gary's took Tecumseh (their Indian statue), what did they do to shut down Gary's?
    A. They stole all of Gary's liquor.
    B. They barricaded his door shut.
    C. They put up "Toxic Waste" signs at Gary's.

16. When it turned out that Gary's did not take Tecumseh, the gang decided to get themselves before Gary's could get them. What did they do?

17. Fraiser and Lilith took Carla and her son, Ludlow, to a very formal restaurant. Ludlow refused to eat and crawled under the table. What did he then do to Fraiser's shoe?

18. Whose gold card did Norm and Cliff trick Sam into destroying?

19. On Halloween night, the gang put what in Gary's bar that supposedly scared Gary to death?
    A. A skeleton
    B. A coffin that talked
    C. A hologram of Carla's head

20. What happened after Sam finally accepted Gary's death?

21. What did Carla arrange to drop on Rebecca's head when she entered her office?

22. Rebecca tried to get even with Carla for trapping her in the heating duct by throwing Carla's purse into the duct. What did Rebecca then discover?

23. Gary's bar appeared to be under new management headed by Frank Carpaccio. With what organization was he supposed to be connected?

24. After the gang decorated Carpaccio's bar with toilet paper, how did he retaliate?

25. Some of the gang were convinced to leave town to avoid Carpaccio and were dropped off in the middle of nowhere by fake FBI agents. Who was behind the whole Carpaccio scam?

Answers

1. She clucked like a chicken.

2. Gary's Olde Towne Tavern

3. Robert Desiderio

4. Bowling

5. Bowling

6. Diane

7. They left him in the woods.

8. Leave the guys in the woods

9. On Woody's head

10. Best Bloody Mary

11. They served the champagne in dribble glasses.

12. He shortened them.

13. Sheep

14. A nun

15. C. They put up "Toxic Waste" signs.

16. They shaved their heads in mohawks to spell G-A-R-Y.

17. He lit it on fire.

18. Frasier's

19. C. A hologram of Carla's head

20. Gary appeared disguised as Woody.

21. A bucket of water

22. She had thrown her own purse in.

23. The Mob

24. He blew up Cheers's front door.

25. Sam

13

Guest Stars

Questions

1. What *Night Court* star appeared occasionally as Harry the Hat, a hustler?

2. What famous football player appeared as a sportscaster friend of Sam's (he had also been considered for the role of Sam)?

3. What *Seinfeld* star made a bet with Sam that he couldn't marry Jacqueline Bisset?

4. What *Moonlighting* star played Coach's daughter?

5. What writer and talk show host encouraged Sam to write his memoirs?

6. What *Night Court* star appeared as Diane's childhood friend who was accused of flirting with Sam?

7. What *Mary Poppins* star appeared as Diane's mother?

8. What *Punky Brewster* star appeared as a dying man who gave the gang $100,000?

9. What *Taxi* star played a famous artist who painted Diane's portrait?

10. What speaker of the House of Representatives appeared as himself?

11. What *Night Court* star appeared as one of Carla's high school friends?

12. What *Taxi* star played Diane's friend from the mental institution who became obsessed with Sam?

13. Who starred as Councilwoman Eldridge?

14. What former senator and presidential candidate appeared as Councilwoman Eldridge's friend and Sam's Trivial Pursuit partner?

15. What *Alf* star appeared as Councilwoman Eldridge's opponent who became interested in Diane?

16. What famous English comic appeared as a famous marriage counselor who counseled Sam and Diane not to get married?

17. What *Spenser: For Hire* star appeared as himself?

18. What real-life baseball player did Gary (of Gary's Olde Towne Tavern) trick Cheers into pantsing?

19. What Emmy award-winning actress from *Family* played Carla's mother?

20. Boston's Mayor Raymond L. Flynn appeared on the show. What part did he play?

21. What (Bob) *Newhart* star played Norm's overly devoted secretary?

22. Who starred as Rebecca's former business school professor?

23. Once each year on Valentine's Day, Sam met a particular woman for a romantic getaway. What *Get Smart* star played the woman?

24. What singer did Robin have sing *"You've Lost That Loving Feeling"* to Rebecca?

25. What famous actor's son appeared as Kelly's boyfriend?

26. Who played Kelly's grandmother?

27. What *Wings* star delivered a letter to Carla following Eddie's death?

Diane takes a sudden interest in politics when Sam begins dating a candidate for city council, so she supports the competitor, Jim Fleener (Max Wright). (*AP/Wide World Photos*)

28. What Oscar-winning actress starred as Nanny Gee, Frasier's first wife?

29. What famous actor and producer played Sid Nelson, the owner of the Hungry Heifer?

30. What Massachusetts senator did Norm and Cliff mistake for a news anchorman?

31. Who starred as a rival bar owner and mob boss?

32. Who played the former owner of Cheers?

33. What member of the Kennedy family did Norm try to get a picture of, only to have her take a picture of Norm and Cliff instead?

34. What contemporary crooner appeared as Woody's cousin?

35. What *China Beach* star played the widow of the man who bought Sam's Corvette?

36. What member of the *Little Rascals* appeared as himself?

37. After listening to Norm and Cliff argue about the Boston Garden, what Boston Celtic became obsessed with counting the number of bolts in the parquet floor?

Answers

1. Harry Anderson

2. Fred Dryer

3. Michael Richards

4. Allyce Beasley

5. Dick Cavett

6. Markie Post

7. Glynis Johns

8. George Gaynes

9. Christopher Lloyd

10. Tip O'Neill

11. Marsha Warfield

12. Carol Kane

13. Kate Mulgrew

14. Gary Hart

15. Max Wright

16. John Cleese

17. Robert Urich

18. Wade Boggs

19. Sada Thompson

20. Boston's mayor

21. Cynthia Stevenson

22. Alexis Smith

23. Barbara Feldon

24. Bill Medley

25. Tyrone Power, Jr.

26. Celeste Holm

27. Thomas Hayden Church

28. Emma Thompson

29. Sheldon Leonard

30. Senator John Kerry

31. Harry Guardino

32. Pat Hingle

33. Ethel Kennedy

34. Harry Connick, Jr.

35. Dana Delaney

36. Spanky McFarland

37. Kevin McHale

14

Memorable Quotes

Questions

1. Who said: "I can not be bought and I can not be threatened, but put the two together and I am your man"?

2. Who said: "A lot of people may not know this, but I happen to be quite famous"?

3. Complete this quote from Coach, after Cliff angrily threw Coach's tie into a cocktail-filled blender: "Anyone want a _____-_____?"

4. Complete this quote from Diane about Sam's brother: "He's a man just like any other man you would meet in _____.?
   A. Greek mythology
   B. Your fantasies
   C. New York

5. Who said: "Blackouts are kind of a nice break in the day"?

6. Whose come-on line was Diane referring to when she said: "You know what bothers me—there are women upon whom this works, and they're allowed to vote and drive a car"?

125

7. To whom was Cliff referring when he said: "If we had given as much money to the space program as we have given to that guy, we would have condos on Venus"?

8. Whom was Diane referring to when she said: "High praise, coming from a man who thinks mashed potatoes are a finger food"?

9. Who said: "In high school, I was voted the girl most likely to marry into old money"?

10. Who said: "I think I am going to be pregnant the rest of my life, just like it says in my yearbook"?

11. To whom was Sam referring when he said: "You are the nuttiest, the stupidest, the phoniest fruitcake I have ever met"?

12. Who said: "People don't have to draw pictures for me—although I like it, but they don't have to"?

13. To whom was Norm referring when he said: "You two are lovely, special people, alone, separately, individually. Together, you stink"?

14. Complete this quote from Cliff, during a conversation in which the gang was critical of Sam for being late: "If the _____ _____ ran its business the way you run yours...never mind."

15. Who said: "I don't know where you guys got the idea I'm some passive, easygoing lump"?

16. Whom was Cliff referring to when he said: "Someday that man's head will open up and a prize will pop out"?

Sam is fiercely attracted to a beautiful English lady, Carolyn, (guest star Camilla Moore), the daughter of the new waitress (pictured above), though Carla warns him not to mix business with pleasure. (*AP/Wide World Photos*)

17. Complete this quote by Coach: "It's Cheers; it's a romantic bar—as many people fall in love here as get _____ here."

18. Who said: "It's a sad world when Sam Malone becomes the voice of reason"?

19. Who said: "All great friendships start with one small act of vengeance"?

20. Who said: "A guy doesn't have to do all kinds of macho stuff to prove he's a man. A real man just has to score heavy with the babes"?

21. Who said: "Sam, if I am ever in a life-and-death situation, and things look hopeless, like there's no way of getting out alive, I want you there with me"?

22. Whom was Ma Clavin talking to when she said: "You are my pride and joy, the best thing that ever happened to me. Gee, think of that"?

23. Referring to his undershorts binding up on him, who said: "I'll give them five minutes—sometimes they self-correct"?

24. Who said: "Nothing is ever obvious to me"?

25. Complete this quote from Diane, after Sam threatened to "bounce you off every wall in this office": "Try it and you will be walking _____ tomorrow."

26. Complete this quote. After Cliff promised to deliver the Postal Service vote for a candidate, Carla said: "Too bad it will go to the wrong _____."

27. During Frasier and Diane's wedding, what was Diane's reply when asked if she would marry Frasier?
    A. "Would you repeat the question?"
    B. "I'm thinking."
    C. "Are you speaking to me?"

28. Who said: "Just like all women—if they're not turning down your proposal of marriage, they're accusing you of suspicious behavior in the lingerie changing room"?

29. Complete this quote from Carla: "When one lousy bar can't produce four decent bowlers, it is time for _____ to take a long, hard look at itself."

30. Who gave Woody the following advice: "Never trust a man who can't look you in the eye, never talk when you can listen, and never spend venture capital on a limited partnership without a detailed analytical fiduciary prospectus"?

31. To whom was Sam referring when he said: "The first time I saw you I said to myself, 'Now that could be the woman who could make me happy the rest of my life.' Now I'd be happy just to stay out of jail"?

32. Who said: "There are two approaches a woman can take to turning her looks to her advantage, and the first is to play upon the male sexual drive and turn yourself into an object of desire. I have opted for the second: scaring them stupid"?

33. To whom was Carla talking when she said: "At least get the tension in the [hair] bun checked—if that baby goes we're all dead"?

34. Complete this remark from Norm to Cliff: "You are a walking encyclopedia; unfortunately, you are also a _____ encyclopedia."

35. Who said: "I'm a guy: I'm _supposed_ to be a big baby"?

36. Why did Lilith say: "Lay your hands upon me, everyone, I am life"?

37. Complete this quote from Sam: "Good looks open doors; good _____ blows them off their hinges."

38. Complete this quote from Norm: "I haven't opened my mail in a while; once my _____ ran out all of the incentive was gone."

39. Who said: "I have accomplished some legendary feats in my time, but this is my masterpiece, my Moaning Lisa"?

40. To whom was Lilith talking when she said: "That hardly seems just, coming from a woman whose hair has never seen a greasy pot it couldn't scrub clean"?

41. Who said: "I don't have a thing against Halloween, I just don't want my son panhandling door-to-door accepting nonnutritious snacks, dressed in a silly costume"?

42. Who said: "Let's get this bris on the road, chop-chop. Oh, wrong choice of words"?

43. Complete this quote from Frasier: "You're all suffering from the winter blues: the shortened daylight hours, the cold, numbing weather, the bleak sense of

isolation. It's what we in the psychiatric profession call the _____."

44. When Cliff said, "I am ashamed God made me a man," who said: "I don't think God is doing a lot of bragging about it either"?

45. Complete this quote from Frasier: "If you can't _____ at your patients, what fun are they?"

46. Who said: "Gee, I don't know what to tell you; then again, I don't know what to tell most people"?

47. Complete this quote from Sam: "I didn't want to be a bad sport, I just wanted to do anything I had to to _____."

48. Who said: "My marriage is my most prized possession—in fact, next to my Honda Civic, my only possession"?

49. To what was Frasier referring when he said: "Now there is a head I can shrink"?

50. Whom was Rebecca referring to when she said: "I would rather remove my own gallbladder with an oyster fork than go out with you"?

51. Who said: "Woody, I don't think I have ever tried to hide the fact that I dislike you intensely"?

52. When Lilith talked about the danger of overprotecting children, who said: "You've got to watch that, that will really screw a kid up!"

53. Complete this quote from Sam: "After ten months of _____ I couldn't even pronounce my name."

54. Complete this quote from Norm: "Great looks and all that savvy, Sam—if you had a _____ in the middle of your forehead, I would marry you in a second."

55. Complete this quote from Mr. Gaines: "Mussolini could not have been all bad, if he had his own son-in-law _____."

56. To what was Frasier referring when he said: "I have also realized that if I was to do it for any amount of time, you would hear stories of me sitting naked in a tower with a high-powered rifle."?
    A. Dating Diane
    B. Counseling Cliff
    C. Baby-sitting

57. Complete this quote from Cliff: "_____ _____ are pretty much the Indiana Joneses of the civil service."

58. Complete this quote from Frasier. "From our 'Things You Thought You Would Never Hear' category, that woman is carrying _____ child."

59. Who gave the following eulogy at Gary's funeral: "Get out of there, Gary!"

60. Who said: "I'm not bitter, I'm just consumed by a gnawing hate that is eating away at my gut until I can taste the bile in my mouth"?

61. To whom was Norm talking when he said: "Walt Disney should have your imagination"?

62. Complete this quote from Cliff: "The harp is the grandfather of the modern-day guitar. It seems that the early minstrels were much larger people; they had hands the size of small _____."

63. Whom was Frasier referring to when he said: "She is a good woman—strong, durable, reliable"?

64. To whom was Rebecca talking when she said: "You're the closest thing to a sailor I know"?

65. Who said: "Yes, there is nothing young women find more attractive than a middle-aged man carrying a rat in a cage"?

66. Who said: "I am not a robot"?

67. Who sarcastically said: "I am filling Woody's shoes. Oh, the pressure!"

68. Whom was Diane referring to when she said: "She's the emotional equivalent of Mr. Toad's wild ride"?

69. Who said: "That's all I've done my whole life is think, think, think. There comes a time when you have to stop thinking; you taught me that, Sam"?

70. At Woody's wedding. Sam asked Lilith to sing and dance and entertain the guests with her natural talents. Complete this quote from Lilith: "Oh my God, someone has _____."

71. When Cliff's former girlfriend showed up pregnant, who said: "You are going to marry her, aren't you; it would be a shame to have to stone her"?

72. Complete this quote from Frasier: "We've just made one horrible mistake—we left the child alone with its _____."

73. When Norm gets a job at a brewery, what did he say to one of the large tanks of beer?

74. When Cheers burned down, who said: "Well, I see you monkeys have discovered fire"?

75. Who said: "Until he finds out how screwed up I am and dumps me, we are going to have the most wonderful marriage"?

76. Whom was Norm referring to when he said: "I gave that man the best years of my life"?

Answers

1. Norm

2. Sam

3. Mai-Tai

4. A. Greek mythology

5. Coach

6. Sam's

7. Harry the Hat

8. Sam

9. Diane

10. Carla

11. Diane

12. Coach

13. Sam and Diane

14. Post Office

15. Norm

16. Coach

17. Sick

18. Diane

19. Carla

20. Sam

21. Woody

22. Cliff

23. Norm

24. Coach

25. Funny

26. Address

27. C. "Are you speaking to me?"

28. Cliff

29. America

30. Woody's father

31. Diane

32. Lilith

33. Lilith

34. Talking

35. Sam

36. She was pregnant.

37. Hair

38. Unemployment [checks]

39. Sam

40. Carla

41. Lilith

42. Frasier

43. Jackpot

44. Carla

45. Laugh

46. Woody

47. Win

48. Norm

49. A mug of beer

50. Sam

51. Mr. Gaines, Woody's father-in-law

52. Cliff

53. Celibacy

54. (Beer) Spigot

55. Shot

56. C. Baby-sitting

57. Postal carriers

58. Cliff's

59. Sam

60. Woody

61. Cliff

62. Dogs

63. Lilith

64. Carla

65. Frasier

66. Lilith

67. Henri, Woody's French nemesis

68. Rebecca

69. Woody

70. Died

71. Woody

72. Mother

73. "Honey, I'm home"

74. John Allen Hill

75. Rebecca

76. Sam

15

Last Call:
The Last Season

Questions

1. Rebecca vowed to turn her life around and not screw up ever again. She was going to start by not smoking anymore. What happened to her last cigarette?

2. Carla took a temporary job at another bar. She was going to stay, but when she saw her new trainee, she ran screaming from the bar. What was it about the new trainee?

3. Cliff's mailbag, full of mail, was destroyed in the bar. How did he cover it up?

4. Norm was offered money by a market researcher to taste various beers. What did Norm ask the researcher?
   A. If he had been born in a manger
   B. If they were on *Candid Camera*
   C. If it was Christmas already

5. While tasting various beers, what did Norm ask for to cleanse his palate?

6. What did Norm try to do with his first paycheck from the brewery?

7. After tasting beer all day at the brewery, what did Norm want to do to rest?

8. For which of the following reasons did Henri want Sam to turn him down for a job?
   A. So he could collect unemployment payments
   B. So he could watch TV all day
   C. So he could stay in this country

9. When a bearded and grubby Robin Colcord returned to Cheers, Cliff mistook him for a mysterious person he had been tracking for years. Who?
   A. D. B. Cooper
   B. Jimmy Hoffa
   C. Butch Cassidy

10. Why was Robin penniless?
    A. He lost all his money in real estate.
    B. He was forced to give it all to his fellow prison inmates.
    C. He felt money caused greed and took a vow of poverty.

11. What did the gang do when they suspected Robin had hidden another money belt in the bar?

12. Why was Rebecca so nice to Robin after he returned penniless?

13. Sam continually refused Henri's challenge to see who could collect the most phone numbers from women. What changed Sam's mind?
    A. Henri called Sam a scaredy-cat.
    B. The women started to ask Sam for his phone number.
    C. Henri insulted the U.S.A.

The cast of *Cheers* celebrating their 200th episode. Back row,
from left: John Ratzenberger, Rhea Perlman, Roger Rees, Kirstie
Alley, Ted Danson, Woody Harrelson, Shelley Long, George
Wendt. Front row, left - right: Kelsey Grammer, Bebe Neuwrith.
(*AP/Wide World Photos*)

14. Who lost the contest, but left the bar with three women?

15. With whom did Lilith admit to having an affair?

16. Where did Lilith and her new love go to live?

17. When Frasier attempted suicide over the loss of Lilith, the police were unable to contact their suicide-prevention psychologist. Who was the psychologist?

18. Norm and Cliff took Frasier and Woody to a drive-in theater before it was torn down. What film festival was showing at the drive-in?

19. The car they took ended up being wrecked. To whom did it belong?

20. When the previous owner of Cheers came for a visit, what did Sam let him do?

21. Where did the gang get their place settings for their Thanksgiving dinner?

22. Why did Sam toast Hill at the Thanksgiving dinner?
    A. He liked Hill.
    B. He felt guilty about the place settings.
    C. He saw Hill coming down the stairs.

23. Rebecca thought that Mr. Gaines had invited her to his home on a date. What was his true intention?

24. Cheers and Gary's Olde Towne Tavern had a bet on who would do the most business on St. Patrick's Day. What did Gary's "wall up" at Cheers, preventing it from opening for business?

25. Since Cheers lost the bet, the guys had to sing at Gary's. What did they have to wear?

26. When Gary thought he had sold his bar to a commercial developer, what did he do as part of the deal?

27. Who had posed as the developer?

28. Having sold his Corvette earlier to raise money, how was Sam able to buy it back?

29. Rebecca's father came for a visit and threatened to take her home in an effort to trick her into giving up her allowance. What did Rebecca do?

30. In what branch of the service was Rebecca's father?

31. What was Rebecca's father's solution for getting the Gilligan's Island crew off the island?
    A. Build a raft
    B. Light signal fires
    C. Shoot Gilligan

32. With whom did Frasier begin an affair just as Lilith returned from the experimental city?

33. Why did Pascal (Lilith's lab partner) follow Lilith from the experimental city back to Boston and hold the gang hostage?

34. Which of the following difficulties did Pascal have while in the underground city?
    A. He had claustrophobia.
    B. He had an imaginary friend.
    C. He snored.

35. To prove that voters are gullible, Frasier proposed that even a simpleton could get ten percent of the vote in a city council election. Whom did he get to run?

36. What happened during Frasier's dream about Woody being president?
    A. Woody moved the nation's capital to Hanover, Indiana.
    B. Woody sold the country to Japan.
    C. Woody started a nuclear war.

37. What did Kelly tell Woody during his city council debate?

38. Who won the city council election?

39. Cliff's former girlfriend, Maggie, returned from Canada with a surprise for him. What?

40. Sam was reluctant to have Carla tend bar because she made the drinks to strong. Which of the following did he say happened the last time she tended bar?
    A. The patrons formed a naked conga line outside the bar.
    B. They tried to sell the bar.
    C. Norm was put in charge of the tabs.

41. Carla said her drinks would be so strong "you will never recognize you own friend." Who asked for a double?

42. After having Carla's strong drinks, Cliff woke up so hung over he did not know where he was, so he called Sam at the bar for help. Where was Cliff?

43. After sobering up, Norm and Cliff discovered that they had been tattooed. What was Norm's tattoo?

44. What was Cliff's tattoo?

45. What did Cliff offer to do with his tattoo"?

46. What did Cliff want Norm to do with his?

47. To illustrate that everyone has secrets, what did Sam reveal to Carla?

48. Cliff claimed that his mother's retirement home was famous, because he saw it on what TV program?
    A. *The Lawrence Welk Show*
    B. *Lifestyles of the Rich and Famous*
    C. *60 Minutes*

49. Rebecca fell in love with a repairman. What did he repair?

50. Who appeared as the repairman?

51. In the series finale, what award did Diane win?

52. During her acceptance speech, for what did Diane thank her parents?

53. What did Diane and Sam lie to each other about?

54. For what did Diane say she had waited before returning to Cheers?

55. After reconciling with Diane, Sam decided it was time to move on with his life. Where did he decide to go?

56. After Sam realized his mistake, where did he go?

57. Norm said he knew Sam would return to his true love. He knew Sam would always be faithful to what?

58. What did Norm not want to go to heaven without?

59. Before Sam left the bar, what picture did he straighten?

60. To whom had the picture belonged?

61. Sam spoke the last words of the series. What were they?

Answers

1. It burned down the bar.

2. She was a Diane look-alike.

3. He staged a fake (Postal) jeep accident.

4. A. If he had been born in a manger

5. Pizza

6. Give it back

7. Go to Cheers and drink beer.

8. A. and B. So he could collect unemployment payments *and* watch TV all day

9. A. D. B. Cooper

10. C. He felt money caused greed, and took a vow of poverty.

11. They tore apart the bar looking for it.

12. She thought that he was secretly rich.

13. C. Henri insulted the U.S.A.

14. Sam

15. Her lab associate, Dr. Pascal

16. In an experimental underground city

17. Frasier

18. Godzilla

19. Ma Clavin

20. Sam let him run the bar for the night.

21. Melville's

22. C. He saw Hill coming down the stairs.

23. To have her tend bar

24. The bar area

25. Nothing

26. He bulldozed his bar.

27. Harry the Hat

28. The owner died, and Sam bought it back from the widow.

29. Rebecca agreed to go, tricking him into raising her allowance.

30. Navy

31. C. Shoot Gilligan

32. Rebecca

33. He wanted Lilith back.

34. A. and B. He had claustrophobia *and* an imaginary friend.

35. Woody

36. C. Woody started a nuclear war.

37. That she was pregnant

38. Woody

39. She was pregnant.

40. A. The patrons formed a naked conga line outside the bar.

41. Norm

42. In Sam's office

43. An American flag with the words: "God Bless the U.S. Postal Department"

44. A big heart with the words: "I Love Vera"

45. Show Vera

46. Show Cliff's supervisor

47. That he wore a hairpiece

48. C. *60 Minutes*

49. Beer taps

50. Tom Berenger

51. Best Writing for Cable TV

52. Conceiving and bearing her

53. Being married and having children

54. She wanted to become successful first.

55. To Hollywood with Diane

56. He returned to Cheers.

57. Cheers

58. His bar stool

59. Geronimo

60. Nicholas Colasanto (Coach)

61. "Sorry, we're closed."